nickelodeon

pinkfong
BABY SHARK™

JUMBO
COLORING AND ACTIVITY BOOK

SHARK-TASTIC!

bendon®

nickelodeonjr.tv

HOW MANY?

How many starfish do you see?

ANSWER:

ANSWER: 6

SHADOW MATCH

Find the shadow that matches Grandpa Shark.

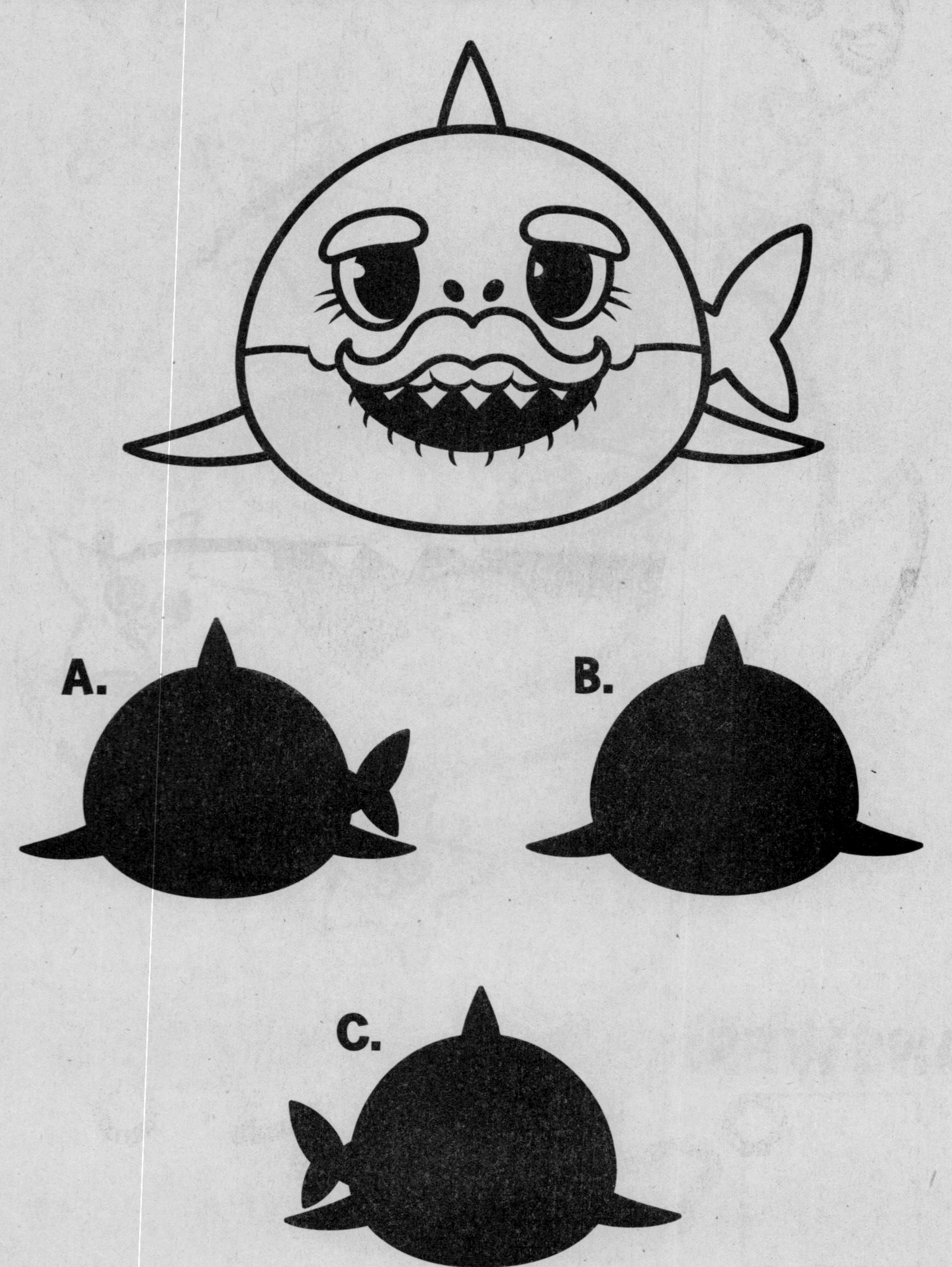

ANSWER: A

Write the first part of the sea creature's name.

STAR FISH

JELLY FISH

PUFFER FISH

SPOT THE DIFFERENCE

Find the 3 differences between the two pictures.

ANSWERS: Daddy Shark's belly is filled, no spots on William, and no tongue on Baby Shark.

CROSSWORD

Fill in the words from the word list to complete the crossword puzzle.

Word List

- Baby
- Daddy
- Mommy
- Sand
- Shark
- Shell
- Water
- Wave

ANSWER: Across - 3. BABY, 4. SHELL, 6. WATER, 7. DADDY
Down - 1. MOMMY, 2. WAVE, 4. SHARK, 5. SAND

MATCHING

Take a look at all four pictures. Which two are the same?

A.

B.

C.

D.

ANSWER:

ANSWER: A AND D

BEGINNING SOUNDS

Trace the SH to complete each word.

SH ARK

FI SH

BRU SH

SH ELL

WORD SEARCH

Look up, down and across for the words in the word list.

Word List

Eye	Skin
Fin	Tail
Flipper	Teeth

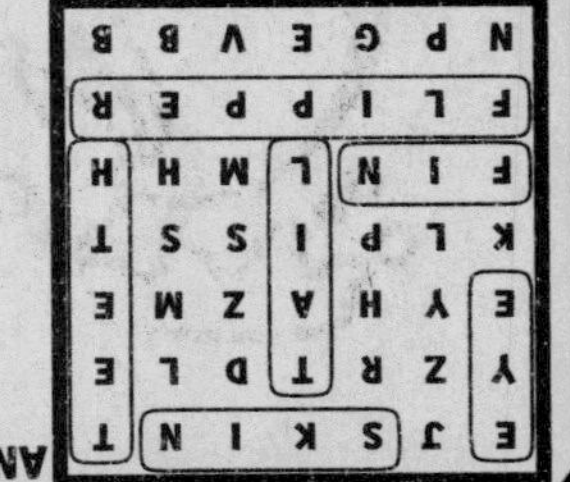

Color the number 3s below.
How many did you find?

Look at the object then trace the word.

ALL ABOUT ME!
My name is
I am
years old.
This is me!
I love...

F

Color the objects that begin with the letter F.

ANSWER: THE FISH AND FORK

HOW MANY?

How many music notes do you see?

ANSWER:

ANSWER: 7

Grandma Shark

Grandpa Shark

Draw a line to connect the matching objects.

TRACING

Trace the path that leads Baby Shark to Mommy Shark!

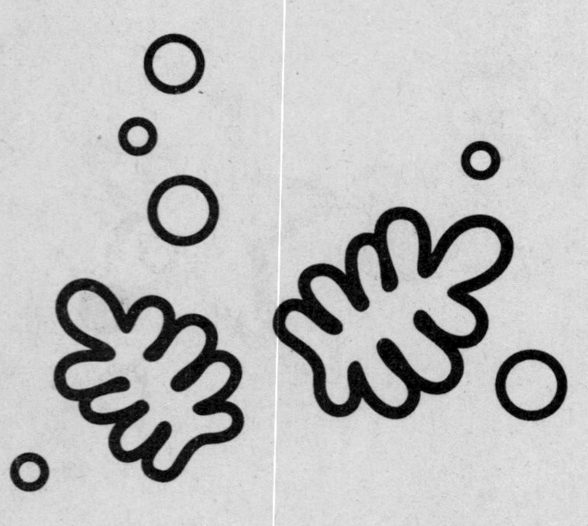

RHYME TIME

Circle the words that rhyme with:

HAT

FIN

BAT

PAT

SEA

MAT

EYE

SHADOW MATCH

Find the shadow that matches William.

A.

B.

C.

ANSWER: C

Circle the beginning sound for each object.

A P F T

Y S O R

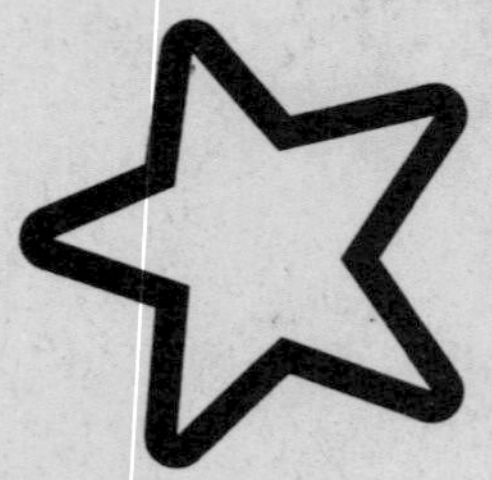

T N S M

C B L M

TIC TAC TOE

Use these tic-tac-toe grids to challenge your family and friends!

COUNT & MATCH

Count the objects in each row then draw a line to connect the matching number.

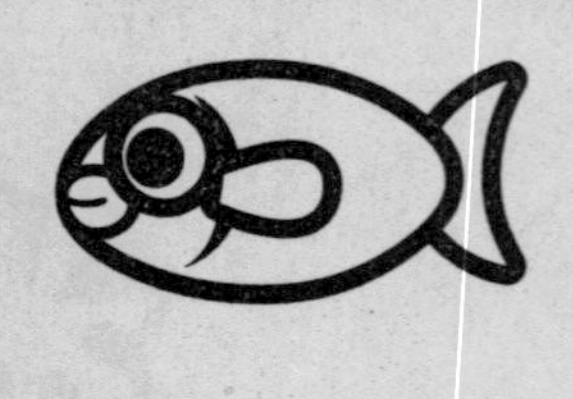

Color Mommy Shark. Then practice printing the word mommy.

MOMMY

Draw a line from each shark to his or her shadow.

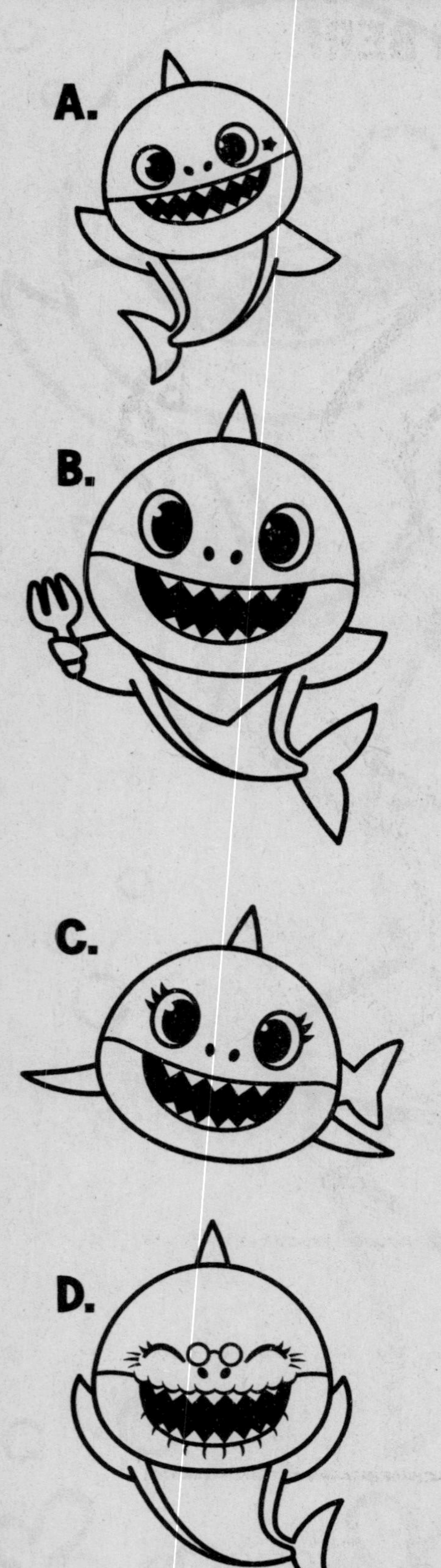

Color Mommy Shark. Then practice printing the word BERRY.

Beach day!

Color the number 4s.
How many did you find?
5 3 4 3 4 1 4 5 2 4 3 4 6 1 4
Your Answer:
Answer: 6

Floating is FINtastic!

TRACING

Trace the path that leads Daddy Shark to Mommy Shark!

Color Baby Shark. Then practice printing the name Baby Shark.

BABY

SHARK

HOW MANY?

How many crabs do you see?

ANSWER:

ANSWER: 5

Sweet!

HOW MANY?

How many shells do you see?

ANSWER:

ANSWER: 7

Stay cool!

Color the tree. Then practice printing the word TREE.

Color the number 5s.
How many did you find?
Your Answer:
Answer: 4

TIC TAC TOE

Use these tic-tac-toe grids to challenge your family and friends!

TRACING

Trace the path that leads Grandma Shark to Grandpa Shark!

SHADOW MATCH

Find the shadow that matches Mommy Shark.

ANSWER: B

Sea you next time!